THE RIGHT TOOL

All four tool boxes may look the same, but each box has one tool that the others don't. Can you find the four individual tools?

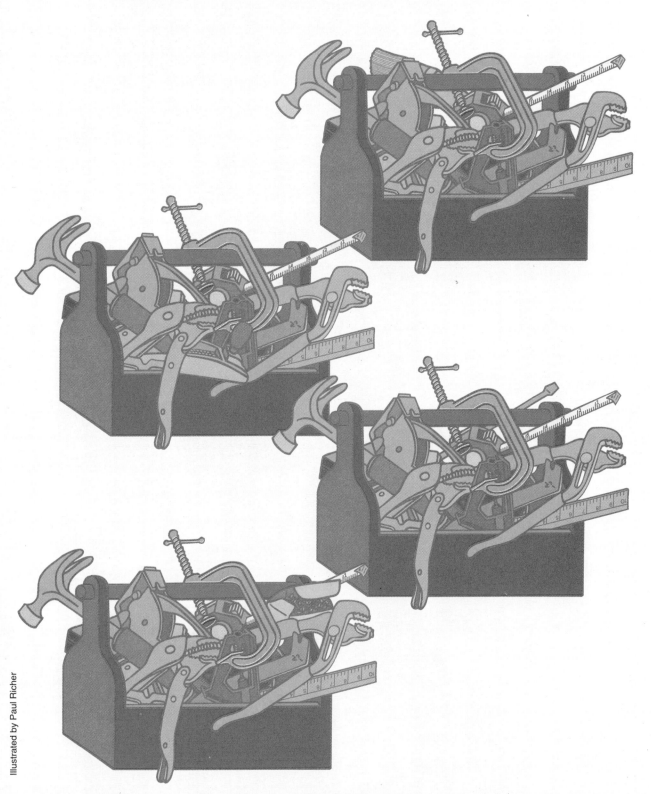

Illustrated by Paul Richer

Answer on page 47.

TIME TEASERS

Rebus Rita left her schedule on the refrigerator door. Can you tell where she's supposed to go or what she's going to do, as well as what time she's supposed to be at each place?

NOAH SCAPE

How many unusual things do you see here?

INSTANT PICTURE

Hold on tight as you try to fill in each section that contains two dots.

Answer on page 47.

GARDEN PARTY

Read the clues and then put your answers in the boxes on the next page. Plant all the answers in the right places and you'll have this garden blooming in no time.

ACROSS

1. Prepare food
4. Water your garden with this
8. Connecting word
9. _____ Ana or Claus
10. Make long marks in the dirt
12. Black, sticky sealant
13. Right at this spot
14. Car's noisemaker or brass instrument
15. Female sheep
16. Duck's mouth and nose
19. Takes part in a play
23. Number of seeds in an avocado
24. Extra
25. Sleek water animal
27. Ocean
28. Throw
29. Red vegetable

DOWN

1. A crop that's grown to sell
2. Word that begins all good fairy tales
3. Smell from something
4. Short laugh
5. Be aware of something going on
6. Polaris is one
7. Make money from selling your vegetables
9. Abbreviation for southeast
11. Part of a fishing rod
14. Large, messy pile
16. Footwear for the garden
17. Enter: go _____
18. Short form of "let us"
20. Something to carry work or clothes in
21. What an arbor contains, singular
22. Something to sit on
24. Abbreviation for senior
26. Plural for some words that end in "s"

Illustrated by Barbara Gray

Answer on page 47

ROW, ROW, ROW

Every lighthouse here has something in common with the two other lighthouses in the same row. For example, each lighthouse in the top row across has a black roof. Look at the other lighthouses across, down, and diagonally. Can you tell what's the same in each row of three?

Illustrated by Dave Phillips

Answer on page 47.

CROP CIRCLES

Something strange is going on out here but maybe you can solve
it by following the path from START to FINISH.

START

FINISH

Illustrated by Charles Jordan

Answer on page 47.

CAT & DOG MYSTERY

Case #536
A Fright at the Opera

Deductive Dog pulled at the stiff collar around his neck. He was dressed in a tuxedo and was very uncomfortable. Clue Cat, squirming in the next seat, didn't look much better.

One night each year, the wives of the two detectives insisted they be taken out to the Arts Night Annual Benefit at the Opera House.

Tonight's performance was 'Turandoe,' and featured Luciano Pigaroutti singing the lead role.

The crowd erupted with applause as the last note was sung. The two detectives were making a dash for the doors when a scream was heard.

"Bring the police!" the unmistakable tenor of Pigaroutti called out. "I've been robbed!"

Dog's ears perked up. Both detectives looked at their wives, who could only sigh.

"Go ahead," Mrs. Dog said. "You won't be happy until you investigate."

"Try not to get your tuxedo dirty," warned Mrs. Cat.

The two detectives ran backstage. After identifying themselves as police officers, they went to Pigaroutti's dressing room.

Pigaroutti was lying on a long couch with a towel over his head.

"My most precious possession has been stolen," he moaned. "I own the world's only copy of the original score to the opera 'Cayman.' I keep it in my dressing room during performances for good luck. And now it's gone."

"Was it insured?" Dog asked.

"What does that matter? The loss of that score is a terrible blow to musicians everywhere."

"Then I suggest we ask the musicians about the theft," Dog said.

The two detectives went to interview some of the musicians who were packing up to head home.

"The score to 'Cayman' has been stolen," Dog said. "Were any of you backstage during tonight's program?"

"Not me," claimed the cello player, a penguin. "I was dressed and ready to go on when I got here."

"It wasn't me," the flamingo who had played the harp said. "I only came back here once to get a copy of 'Die Fleidermaus' in the key of J."

"I came back once to get some polish for my cornet," said a lion. "It's a marvelous brass instrument, don't you agree?"

Cat moved to the ladybug who was next in line and brought her over.

"And where do you think you're going?" Dog asked.

"I'm the tuba player, and I'm exhausted. All I want to do now is fly away home and sleep."

Just then, a very nervous mole came toward the exit, dragging one of the bass drums along behind him. He made a great show of lifting the drum into its case and packing it away securely. Straightening his tuxedo jacket, the mole then headed for the door.

"And what about the score?" Dog asked as the mole came near.

"Uh, three to nothing?" the mole said hesitantly.

"You'll get more like ten to twenty, along with your partner," Clue Cat said as he snapped on the handcuffs. "Both of you have given us the keys to solve this mystery."

You know that Cat grabbed the mole as one suspect. But who else do the detectives think might be involved?

Now that you've recovered the missing music, help Dog & Cat locate all the instruments hidden in the scene.

WEATHER BEATERS

Chart the weather for each day of the first week in June and the
first week in January by working the problems below and then
fitting the answers onto the proper spots on the thermometers.
To work the problems, do each function as you go from left to right.

June

Date
6/1. 187-98 =
6/2. 7 x 7 + 42=
6/3. 420 ÷ 4=
6/4. 68 x 2 + 4 - 72 =
6/5. 7 + 15 x 2 + 32 =
6/6. 5 x 15 + 23 =
6/7. 246 ÷ 3 =

January

Date
1/1. 224 ÷ 7 =
1/2. 187-192 =
1/3. 8 x 21 - 152 =
1/4. 5 + 17 =
1/5. 18+10+12+6 =
1/6. 6 x 17 - 96 =
1/7. 78+4-60-32 =

Illustrated by Terry Kovalcik

Answer on page 48.

THE INSIDE STORY

Each tangled word is actually two words, one tangled inside another. Remove each inside word from its outside word. When you're through, transfer the numbered letters to the spaces below to answer the riddle.

Example: enlettervelope

Letter goes inside an **envelope**

1. egchickeng   _ _ _ _ _ _ _ inside _ _ _ _
                    2

2. cmilkow   _ _ _ _ inside _ _ _ _
                              6

3. caverbatsn   _ _ _ _ inside _ _ _ _ _ _
                                      3

4. chrysabutterflylis   _ _ _ _ _ _ _ _ _

   inside _ _ _ _ _ _ _ _ _
              7

5. balairloon   _ _ _ inside _ _ _ _ _ _ _
                                  5

6. hebrainad   _ _ _ _ _ inside _ _ _ _
                                    4

7. wragumpper   _ _ _ _ inside _ _ _ _ _ _ _
                                  1

Answer on page 48.

What do we use to see outside when inside and inside when outside?

_ _ _ _ _ _ _
1 2 3 4 5 6 7

Illustrated by Jeff Shelly

FIND THE RHYMES

There is a word missing in each nursery-rhyme sentence or in the name of a nursery-rhyme character. The missing words are hidden across, up, down, backward, or diagonally in the letters on the next page. Once you've found all the words, read the uncircled letters from left to right, top to bottom, to discover the name of a famous nursery-rhyme character.

1. It's raining, it's pouring, the old man is __ __ __ __ __ __ __.
2. Wee Willie __ __ __ __ __ __
3. I've been to __ __ __ __ __ __ __ to visit the queen.
4. Mary had a little lamb, its __ __ __ __ __ __ __ was white as snow.
5. Baa, baa, black sheep, have you any __ __ __ __?
6. __ __ __ __ __ __ Piper
7. Yankee __ __ __ __ __ __
8. Ladybug, ladybug, fly away __ __ __ __.
9. The was an old __ __ __ __ __ __ who lived in a shoe.
10. __ __ __ __ __ __ __ Dumpty
11. Ring around the __ __ __ __ __ __, pocketful of posies.
12. Lucy Locket lost her __ __ __ __ __ __.
13. Old Mother Hubbard went to the __ __ __ __ __ __ __ __ __
14. Goosey, goosey __ __ __ __ __ __ __
15. London __ __ __ __ __ __ __ is falling down
16. Little __ __ __ __ __ Muffet
17. __ __ __ __ __ __ Blind Mice, see how they run.
18. Pease porridge hot, pease porridge __ __ __ __.
19. Ding dong __ __ __ __, pussy's in the well.
20. There was a little girl who had a little __ __ __ __

21. Little Bo Peep has __ __ __ __ her sheep
22. Simple __ __ __ __ __ __
23. Little Tommy __ __ __ __ __ __ __
24. Jack __ __ __ __ __ __ could eat no fat.
25. Peter, peter, pumpkin eater, had a __ __ __ __ and couldn't keep her.
26. You used to come at 10:00, now you come at __ __ __ __.
27. To market, to market, to buy a fat __ __ __.
28. Jack and Jill went up the __ __ __ __ __
29. Old King Cole was a merry old __ __ __ __.
30. This is the __ __ __ __ __ __ that Jack built.
31. Little Jack Horner, sat in a corner, eating his Christmas __ __ __.
32. On his face, he __ __ __ __ __ a crooked smile.
33. The __ __ __ __ __ and the unicorn
34. Rub-a-dub- __ __ __

Leftover letters:

__ __ __ __ __ __ __

__ __ __ __ __ __ __

Illustrated by Maurie Jo Manning

S L L E D P E T E R M
Y N H I O W T I H E R
T E O P O C K E T E G
P S M R E N L E F I W
M U E E I D U B O S F
U O R W O N O D N O L
H H E O O O G E L R E
T I D O S M G L U O E
A L N L S D A C O S C
R L A S I M O N S S E
P I G R M R E K C U T
S E B D R A O B P U C

SOCK IT TWO ME

Uh, oh! It's almost time for school and Eric can't find a matching pair of socks. Maybe you'll have better luck. How many pairs of similar socks can you put together?

Answer on page 48.

DOT MAGIC

Join these dots to find a massive monster. Or maybe it's just someone from Minnesota who's looking for a lost squirrel.

Illustrated by John Puntar

Answer on page 48.

HIDDEN PICTURES

There are at least 28 objects hidden in this picture.
How many can you find?

J. Boddy

READ ALL ABOUT IT

Each list below contains three clues that belong together as well as one clue that doesn't belong. It's up to you to tell which clue doesn't belong. Then figure out what you might read that contains the three remaining clues.

1. Highways
   Scale of miles
   Ingredients
   Cities

2. Headline
   Bibliography
   Editorials
   Comics

3. Definitions
   Want ads
   Illustrations
   Pronunciations

4. Recipes
   Ingredients
   Directions
   Lakes

5. Addresses
   Phone Numbers
   Business Ads
   Characters

6. Store Hours
   Names of foods
   Prices
   Oven Temperature

7. Pictures
   Signatures
   Poems
   Table of Contents

8. Clues
   Stock Prices
   Squares
   Numbers

9. Music notes
   Titles
   Lyrics
   Weather forecast

10. Dates
    Chapters
    Months
    Pictures

Illustrated by Gregg Valley

Answer on page 48.

VETERINARIAN MEMORIES

Take a long look at this picture. Try to remember everything you see in it. Then turn the page, and try to answer some questions about it without looking back.

Illustrated by Tim Ellis

DON'T READ THIS UNTIL YOU HAVE LOOKED AT "Veterinarian Memories—Part I" ON PAGE 23.

VETERINARIAN MEMORIES Part II

Can you answer these questions about the veterinarian scene you saw? Don't peek!

1. Are there more animals or people in the scene?
2. How many flying animals are waiting for the vet?
3. What animal came from the circus?
4. How many spotted animals are waiting for the vet?
5. How many people have mustaches?
6. What is the veterinarian saying?
7. What number is on the firefighter's hat?
8. Who brought in a rabbit?
9. How many cats are waiting for the vet?
10. Is anyone reading a magazine?

Answer on page 49.

WORD WHEEL

To learn the answer to this riddle, start at the arrow. Go clockwise around the circle and copy every third letter onto the blanks below.

Riddle: What is it that may have the whole taken away yet some will remain?

___ ___ ___ ___   ___ ___ ___   "___ ___ ___ ___ ___ ___ ___ ___ ___ ___."

Illustrated by Lynn Adams

Answer on page 49.

STOP, LOOK, AND LIST

Under every category, list one thing that begins with each letter. For example, one type of beverage that begins with C is Cola. See if you can name another.

BEVERAGES

C _____

M _____

L _____

T _____

S _____

DEPARTMENT-STORE DEPARTMENTS

C _____

M _____

L _____

T _____

S _____

BOARD GAMES

C _____

M _____

L _____

T _____

S _____

Illustrated by Lisa Dayer

Answer on page 49.

CLOCK FACES

For Granddad's 100th birthday, the Rollecks kids gave him a very special clock. Instead of numbers, a picture of each child adorns the face of the clock. From the information provided can you determine where each child's picture is on the clock?

Illustrated by Patti Argoff

1. Boys are odd-numbered, girls are even-numbered.

2. Going clockwise in order, but starting nowhere in particular, are pictures of Katie, Corey, Allie, Brett, and Sarah.

3. Emily's picture is at the 8 position. Daniel's picture is at the 1 position.

4. Jake is directly opposite Daniel.

5. The clock positions of 12, 3, 6, and 9 are pictures of Sarah, Corey, Samantha, and Steven, but not in this order.

6. Edward is directly between Megan and Samantha.

Answer on page 49.

PICNIC PANIC

You're off on a wonderful picnic! But before you can head out, you have to help pack the picnic basket. Unscramble each of these words to see what you're bringing.

CRYHER IPE

TTOOPA DLASA

PUCS

DRIFE NICHKEC

LOCE LAWS

TRAMLEENOW

SLEPAT

ABDEK ABNES

DOAS

SNAKPIN

CHEWIDANSS

SKORF

BRIEFES

LETKNAB

SLEPAP

TEAMSOOT

Illustrated by Sherry Neidigh

Answer on page 49.

A HOARSE LAUGH

Saddle up, buckaroos, and get ready to ride. Hitch each clue below to one of the letters in the scene in order to answer the riddle.

Letter number eight is on the water trough.

Letter seven is being lassoed.

The sixth letter is on the back of one cowboy's shirt.

Find letter five at the bunkhouse.

Letter four is on the saddle.

Look for letter three on the cow.

The big bronc has letter two on its hoof.

Letter one is on the end of the branding iron.

What sickness do cowpokes get?

___ ___ ___ ___ ___ — ___ ___ ___ ___
1   2   3   4   5   6   7   6   8

Answer on page 49.

Illustrated by Frank Bolle

PILGRIMS' PROGRESS

Can you number the pictures to show what
happened first, second, and so on?

Illustrated by Judith Hunt

Answer on page 49.

MIRROR IMAGE

Mirror, mirror, on this page,
Show us all the current rage.
Use your imagination to draw what's being reflected in this mirror.

Illustrated by M. Gugliotta

DISSIMULATION

Dissimulation is a word that means a gathering or group of birds.
A lot of animal groups have strange names like "herd" or "pack."
The names of 44 different groups of birds can fit into the diagram
shown here. Use the size of each word, as well as similar letters,
as clues to where it will land. When you're done, check the
answer page to find out what type of bird belongs in each group.

3 Letters	4 Letters	5 Letters	6 Letters	7 Letters
nye	bevy	brood	bazaar	bouquet
	cast	charm	covert	company
	dule	covey	flight	descent
	fall	flock	gaggle	deserts
	herd	plump	murder	pitying
	host	siege	muster	
	peep	skein	rafter	
	sord	watch	spring	
	team		tiding	
	walk			
	wisp			

8 Letters	10 Letters	11 Letters	12 Letters
badelyng	chattering	ostentation	congregation
building	exaltation	murmuration	
richness	parliament		
	unkindness		

Illustrated by Anni Matsick

Answer on page 49.

JIGSAW

Can you tell which pieces below belong in the empty spaces?

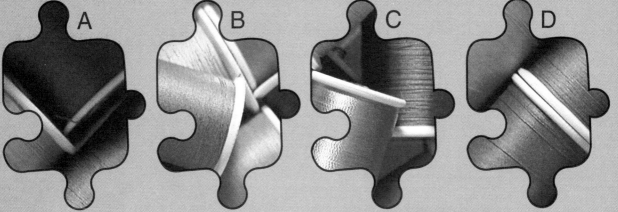

Answer on page 50.

WHAT'S IN A WORD?

The SPECIALTY of this restaurant is alphabet soup. The chef has used the noodle letters to find all the words you can make from the letters in the word SPECIALTY. All the words on our menu are at least three letters long, and none of them are plurals that end in "S." We served up at least 85 words, including words like LACE and SIT. How many can you order?

Answer on page 50.

PICTURE MIXER

Copy these mixed-up squares in the spaces on the next page to put this picture back together. The letters and numbers tell you where each square belongs. The first one, A-3, has been done for you.

A-3   A-4   A-2   A-1

B-2   B-4   B-1   B-3

C-2   C-4   C-3   C-1

D-4   D-3   D-1   D-2

Illustrated by M. Giudietta

Answer on page 50.

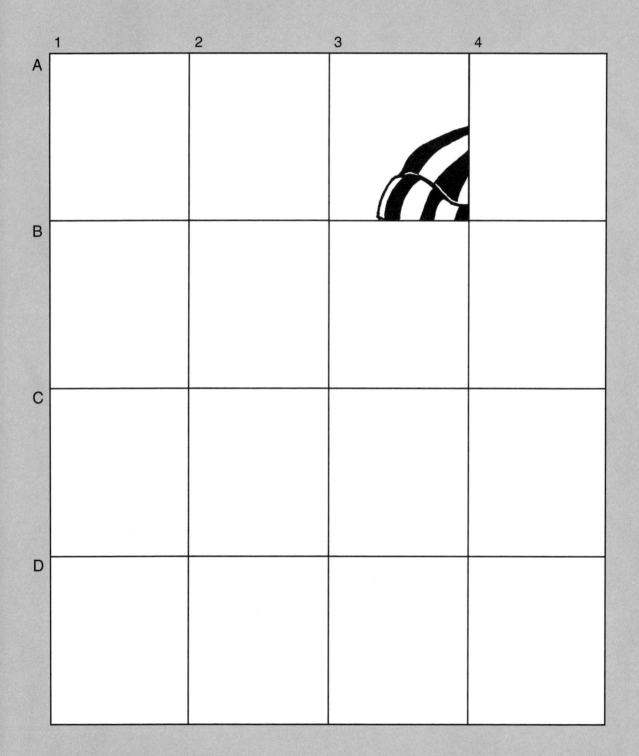

ONE TRACK FIND

Can you find which engine came from which tunnel?

Illustrated by Chuck Dillon

Answer on page 50.

CIRCLE OF LIFE

Things about the human body will complete these circles of life.
Find the missing word that fits in each crescent. Each word has
five letters and each begins in the section where the number
appears. We've done the first one to get you started.

1. _____ cords - air passing
   between these vibrating cords gives
   you your voice.
2. Two-thirds of your body is made of
   this liquid.
3. These cause colds in the body.
4. This sense can identify as many as
   3,000 odors.
5. This delivers oxygen to your cells.
6. Over 200 of these hold
   your body up.

7. This pumps blood through your body.
8. The thinking center
9. This sense helps us look at the
   Moon.
10. The digit that helps you grab things.
11. When your lips curl upward, you do
    this.
12. The funny joint between upper arm
    and lower arm.

Answer on page 50.

TRIBAL TROUBLE

The names of ten Native American chiefs and the tribes they represented are hidden in the grid. To find them, scan each row, going from left to right, and then on to the next row down. Write the letters you find on the rows that match the numbers in each box. We've done the first to start you on the trail.

1. **M A** _ _ _ _ _ _ _ _   _ _ _ _ _ _ _ _

2. _ _ _ _ _ _ _ _   _ _ _ _   _ _ _ _ _

3. _ _ _ _ _ _ _ _   _ _ _ _ _ _

4. _ _ _ _ _ _ _   _ _ _ _ _ _

5. _ _ _ _ _   _ _ _ _   _ _ _ _ _

6. _ _ _ _ _ _ _ _   _ _ _ _ _ _

7. _ _ _ _ _   _ _ _ _ _   _ _ _ _ _

8. _ _ _ _ _   _ _ _ _ _ _ _

9. _ _ _ _ _ _ _   _ _ _ _ _ _

10. _ _ _ _   _ _ _ _ _   _ _ _ _ _ _

40

1 MA	4 PO	3 HI	6 GE	2 SI	8 OS	10 RE	9 TE	5 BL	7 CR
5 AC	2 TT	7 AZ	4 NT	9 CU	1 SS	3 AW	6 RO	10 D	8 CE
2 IN	6 NI	1 AS	8 OL	3 AT	5 KH	7 YH	4 IA	10 BI	9 MS
3 HA	9 EH	4 C	10 RD	1 OI	2 GB	6 MO	8 A	5 A	7 OR
4 O	1 T	5 W	2 UL	7 SE	3 M	10 WI	9 SH	6 A	8 SE
2 L	6 P	1 AL	8 MI	4 T	10 NN	7 S	3 O	5 K	9 A
1 GO	5 S	3 H	9 W	2 SI	8 N	4 T	6 A	10 EB	7 I
4 A	2 O	10 A	1 NQ	6 C	3 A	5 A	7 O	9 N	8 O
5 U	7 U	3 W	6 H	2 U	8 L	1 UI	4 W	10 GE	9 E
2 X	1 N	8 E	4 A	9 E	10 O	6 OE	3 K	5 K	7 X

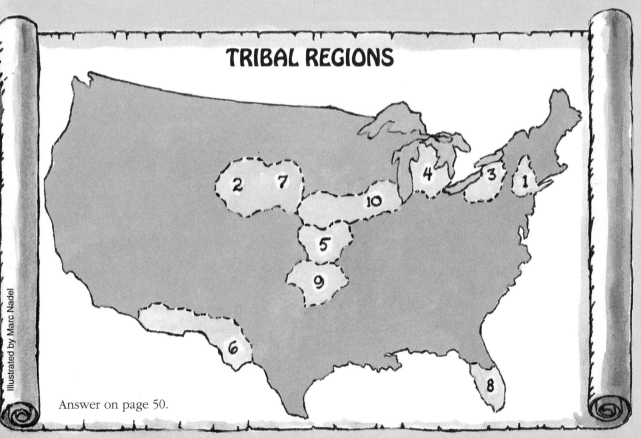

TRIBAL REGIONS

Answer on page 50.

Illustrated by Marc Nadel

DOMINO THEORY

Place the fifteen dominoes onto the big rectangle so that every square is covered. The dots on the dominoes must match the numbers on which each domino is placed. You must use all the dominoes, and each square will be covered only once.

3	1	0	2	4	1
2	3	5	3	0	0
6	3	0	6	0	4
1	0	3	5	5	6
4	3	4	4	2	3

Answer on page 50.

ORE ELSE

The Burrow Brothers are searching for ore–specifically, words that contain the letters O-R-E. Use the clues to see how many ORE words you can identify.

Black-and-white cookie: ORE___

The opposite of less: ___ORE

What a golfer yells: ___ORE

Center of an apple: ___ORE

Achy and tired: ___ORE

Ripped: ___ORE

Place to shop: ___ ___ORE

Where the water meets the sand: ___ ___ORE

Drudge work: ___ ___ORE

The outcome of a ball game: ___ ___ORE

Not after: ___ ___ORE

Dessert for campouts: ___ ___ORE___

Northwestern state: ORE___ ___ ___

Spice for sauce: ORE___ ___ ___ ___

Answer on page 50.

GLOBE PROBE

That intrepid explorer, Dr. Cincinnati Holmes, is always having trouble with his watch. He seldom gets where he's supposed to be, and he's never on time. Can you use the big map to help him answer some of these timely questions? If you find all the correct answers, read the letter of each choice from seven to one to discover the name of an early timepiece.

1. If people in England have high tea at 4:00 P.M., what might people be doing in Chicago?

    j. Eating lunch
    k. Going to bed
    l. Taking a mid-morning break

2. If the people of Paris eat their lunch at noon, what might the residents of Brazil be up to?

    a. Eating breakfast
    b. Having dinner
    c. Watching the 10:00 P.M. news

3. If kids in Iran are just starting at 8:00 A.M., what might the kids in California be doing?

    g. Getting up in time for school
    h. Watching cartoons after school
    i. Getting ready for bed

4. If it's 11:00 P.M. in Japan, what might kids in Alaska be doing?

    d. Sleeping
    e. Doing their work in the classroom
    f. Eating dinner

Illustrated by John Nez

5. If kids in Alabama are watching the last of the Saturday morning cartoons at noon, what might kids in Turkey be doing?

   m. Leaving school   n. Doing homework before bed   o. Dressing for school

6. If kids in New York are watching a snowstorm that began at the predicted time of 2:00 P.M., what mights kids in Australia be doing?

   t. Having an after-school snack   u. Sleeping   v. Eating breakfast

7. If kids in China are eating dinner, what meal are kids eating in Peru?

   q. Dinner   r. Lunch   s. Breakfast

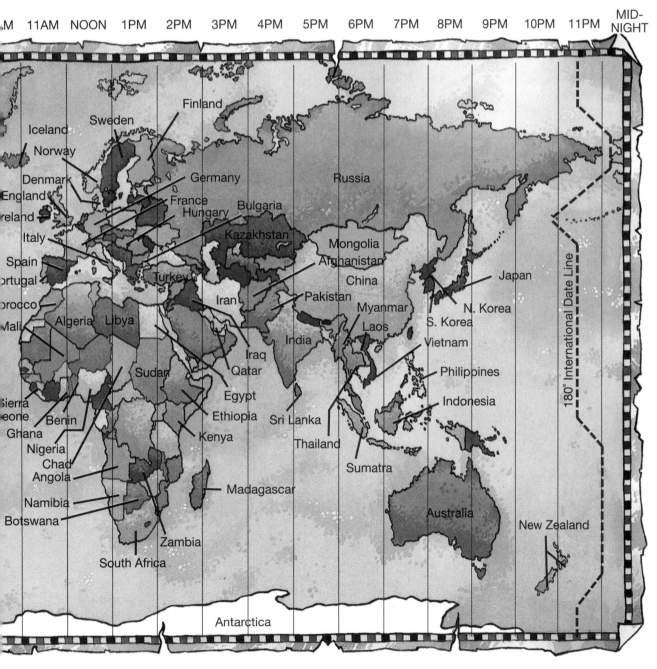

BILLY WHOPPERS

Our Uncle Billy likes to tell stories about his travels. Sometimes these stories are "whoppers," which means he gets carried away and adds a little too much to the story. You can never be sure if he's doing it on purpose or not, but he smiles if you catch his mistake and point it out. See if you can pick out what is unusual or incorrect in each of Billy's whoppers

I love visiting the national parks. The Grand Canyon, Yosemite, or even the Grand Tetons are all spectacular. But one of my favorites is Mount Rushmore. I love looking at those big heads of George Washington, Abraham Lincoln, Franklin Roosevelt, and Thomas Jefferson. Lincoln especially reminds me of my brother, Quincy.

While on vacation last year, I traveled all over the United States. I visited big cities such as Pittsburgh, Detroit, San Francisco, New York, France, Chicago, and Miami.

I once visited the site of a famous airplane flight. Kitty Hawk is where the Wright Brothers are credited with achieving man's first sustained flight. It's funny how the name of the place has two animals in it: Kitty and Hawk. This famous site in North Dakota has become quite a shrine for pilots everywhere.

Answer on page 50.

ANSWERS

THE RIGHT TOOL (page 3)

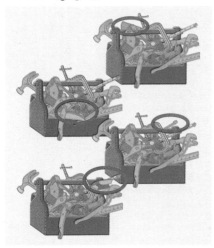

TIME TEASERS (pages 4-5)

1. Breakfast – Half past 8
2. Newspaper route – Ten to 9
3. School – 10 on the dot
4. Doctor – Quarter to 12
5. Piano lessons – One in the afternoon
6. Library – 2:30 (tooth hurty)
7. Dentist – Three P.M.
8. Shopping – Five o'clock
9. Haircut – 7 tonight

INSTANT PICTURE (page 7)

GARDEN PARTY (pages 8-9)

ROW, ROW, ROW (page 10)

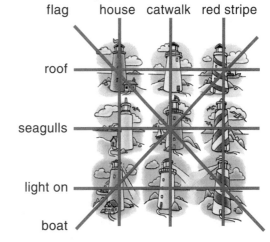

flag   house   catwalk   red stripe

roof

seagulls

light on

boat

CROP CIRCLES (page 11)

CAT & DOG (pages 12-13)

Case #536 - A Fright at the Opera

The mole didn't know that "score" is another word for musical arrangement. Any real musician would know that. The flamingo claimed to be looking for a piece of music in the key of J. Unfortunately for her, the detectives knew that musical scales only go from the key of A to the key of G.

WEATHER BEATERS (page 14)

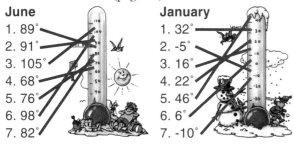

June
1. 89°
2. 91°
3. 105°
4. 68°
5. 76°
6. 98°
7. 82°

January
1. 32°
2. -5°
3. 16°
4. 22°
5. 46°
6. 6°
7. -10°

THE INSIDE STORY (page 15)

1. chicken inside egg
2. milk inside cow
3. bats inside cavern
4. butterfly inside chrysalis
5. air inside balloon
6. brain inside head
7. gum inside wrapper

What do we use to see outside when inside and inside when outside?
WINDOWS

FIND THE RHYMES (pages 16-17)

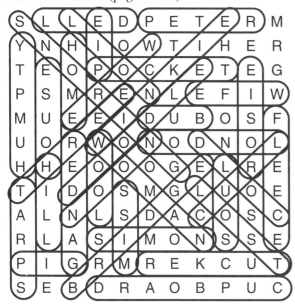

Leftover letters: Mother Goose

SOCK IT TWO ME (page 18)

DOT MAGIC (page 19)

READ ALL ABOUT IT (page 22)

1. Ingredients is the wrong clue. The rest belong to maps.
2. Bibliography is the wrong clue. The rest belong to newspapers.
3. Want ads is the wrong clue. The rest belong to dictionaries.
4. Lakes is the wrong clue. The rest belong to cookbooks.
5. Characters is the wrong clue. The rest belong to telephone books.
6. Oven temperature is the wrong clue. The rest belong to grocery store ads.
7. Table of contents is the wrong clue. The rest belong to greeting cards.
8. Stock prices is the wrong clue. The rest belong to crossword puzzles.
9. Weather forecast is the wrong clue. The rest belong to music books.
10. Chapters is the wrong clue. The rest belong to calendars.

VETERINARIAN MEMORIES (page 24)

1. There are the same amount.
2. Two
3. The bear   7. 17
4. Two   8. The magician
5. Two   9. None
6. "Next…"   10. No

WORD WHEEL (page 24)

What is it that may have the whole taken away yet some will remain? The word "wholesome."

STOP, LOOK, AND LIST (page 25)

Here are our answers. You may have found others.

BEVERAGES	DEPARTMENT–STORE DEPARTMENTS	BOARD GAMES
Coffee	Cosmetics	Clue
Milk	Menswear	Monopoly
Lemonade	Ladies	Life
Tea	Toys	Trouble
Soda	Stationery	Sorry

CLOCK FACES (page 26)

Emily is at number 8 and Daniel is at number 1 (clue 3). Sarah is at 12, 3, 6, or 9 (clue 5). She is not at numbers 3 or 9 (clue 1). If Sarah is at 12, then Katie would be in position 8 (clue 2), but this isn't possible. Therefore, Sarah is at number 6. From clue 2, we now know Katie is at number 2, Corey is at 3, Allie is at 4, and Brett is at 5. Jake must be number 7 (clue 4). Positions 9 and 12 are Steven and Samantha (clues 5 and 1). Edward must be in spot 11 while Megan is in position 10 (clue 6).

PICNIC PANIC (page 27)

Cherry Pie	Plates	Frisbee
Potato Salad	Baked Beans	Blanket
Cups	Soda	Apples
Fried Chicken	Napkins	Tomatoes
Cole Slaw	Sandwiches	
Watermelon	Forks	

A HOARSE LAUGH (pages 28-29)

What sickness do cowpokes get?
BRONC-ITIS

PILGRIMS' PROGRESS (page 30)

4	2
5	6
3	1

DISSIMULATION (pages 32-33)

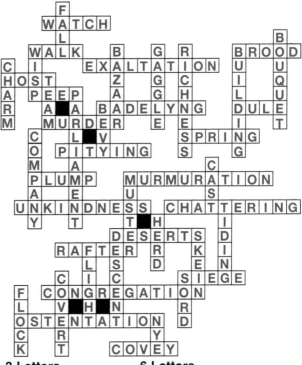

3 Letters
nye (pheasants)

4 Letters
bevy (quail)
cast (hawks)
dule (doves)
fall (woodcocks)
herd (swans)
host (sparrows)
peep (chicks)
sord (mallards)
team (ducks)
walk (snipe)
wisp (snipe)

5 Letters
brood (hens)
charm (finches)
covey (partridges)
flock (ostrich)
plump (wildfowl)
siege (herons)
skein (flying geese)
watch (nightingales)

10 Letters
chattering (choughs)
exaltation (larks)
parliament (owls)
unkindness (ravens)

6 Letters
bazaar (murres)
covert (coots)
flight (swallows)
gaggle (geese)
murder (crows)
muster (storks)
rafter (rafter)
spring (teal)
tiding (magpies)

7 Letters
bouquet (pheasants)
company (widgeon)
descent (woodpeckers)
deserts (lapwings)
pitying (turtledoves)

8 Letters
badelyng (ducks)
building (rooks)
richness (martins)

11 Letters
ostentation (peacocks)
murmuration (starlings)

12 Letters
congregation (plovers)

JIGSAW (page 34)
1 - D, 2 - B, 3 - C, A - Leftover

WHAT'S IN A WORD? (page 35)
Here is our list of 112 words. You may have found others.

ace, act, ail, aisle, ape, ate, aye, cap, cape, case, cast, castle, cat, cay, city, clap, clasp, clay, clip, east, eat, elastic, espy, ice, isle, lace, lap, lapse, last, late, lay, leap, leapt, least, lice, lip, list, pace, pail, pal, pale, past, paste, pastel, pat, pay, pea, peal, peat, pelt, pest, pet, petal, pie, piety, pile, pit, pity, place, plate, play, plea, pleat, ply, sale, salt, sap, sat, say, scale, sea, seal, seat, set, silt, sip, sit, site, slap, slate, slay, slept, slice, slip, slit, sly, space, spay, special, spice, spit, spite, splice, spy, stale, staple, stay, steal, sty, style, talc, tail, tale, tap, tape, tea, tile, tip, type, yeast, yes, yet

PICTURE MIXER (pages 36-37)

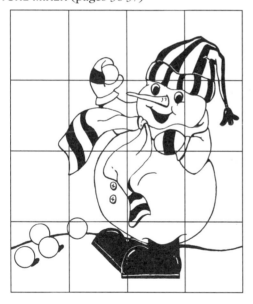

ONE TRACK FIND (page 38)
A – 2
B – 4
C – 1
D – 3

CIRCLE OF LIFE (page 39)
1. Vocal
2. Water
3. Germs
4. Smell
5. Blood
6. Bones
7. Heart
8. Brain
9. Sight
10. Thumb
11. Smile
12. Elbow

TRIBAL TROUBLE (pages 40-41)
1. Massasoit   Algonquin
2. Sitting Bull   Sioux
3. Hiawatha   Mohawk
4. Pontiac   Ottawa
5. Black Hawk   Sauk
6. Geronimo   Apache
7. Crazy Horse   Sioux
8. Osceola   Seminole
9. Tecumseh   Shawnee
10. Red Bird   Winnebago

DOMINO THEORY (page 42)

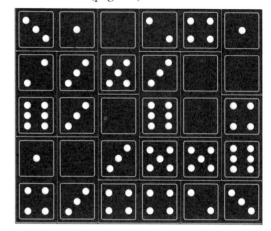

ORE ELSE (page 43)
Oreo
More
Fore
Core
Sore
Tore
Store
Shore
Chore
Score
Before
Smores
Oregon
Oregano

GLOBE PROBE (pages 44-45)
1. l, 2. a, 3. i, 4. d. 5. n, 6. u, 7. s
Ancient timepiece: Sundial

BILLY WHOPPERS (page 46)
1. Theodore Roosevelt is on Mount Rushmore, not Franklin.
2. France is not a city in the United States.
3. Kitty Hawk is in North Carolina.